HARMONY IS FUN

BOOK 1

Claire Liddell

Maureen Cox

First published 1998
by **Subject Publications**
   Beech House
   Broadstone
   Dorset BH18 9NJ
   Tel: +44 (0)1202 696907
   Fax: +44 (0)1202 657743

ISBN 1 898771 11 1

Printed by Pardy & Son (Printers) Ltd.,
Parkside, Ringwood, Hampshire, BH24 3SF
Tel: +44 (0)1425 471433
Fax: +44 (0)1425 478923

Authors' note

Would you like to be able to harmonise a melody? Then you must use your ears to make friends with the members of the musical families.

In this book we use families to introduce harmony in a simple  way. You will meet the **Inner Family** of **Mother**, **Father** and **Daughter**.

The scales or keys are the families and the chords are the family members.

C Major is our central Family and their immediate neighbours are the families of **F Major** and **G Major**.

We should like you to concentrate on making friends with these families and to listen very carefully to the music while you play or sing.

Acknowledgements

We are grateful to Subject Publications for inviting us to write this book and thereby giving us the opportunity to convey to others the excitement and enjoyment of harmony.

We should like to thank our professional colleagues and our students, past and present, for sharing our enthusiasm and encouraging us in this project.

We are especially grateful to Alison Hounsome for her very helpful suggestions and comments.

Claire Liddell & Maureen Cox

CONTENTS

Notes and Keys

The letters A B C D E F G are the names of the notes in the musical alphabet.

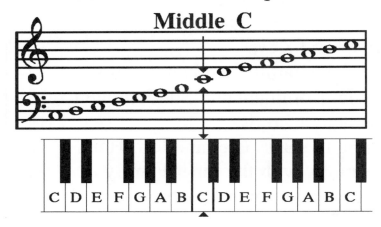

Fingers

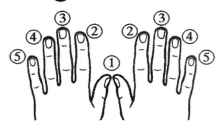

These numbers ①②③④⑤ tell you which fingers you could use.

Remember:

numbers in circles

   are for your fingers.

Meet the Family

Here are the notes in the **C Major** Family.

Here is the mother of the family.

Her note is **C**. She looks after all the notes in the key of **C**.

Mother has a chord.
It is built like this.

A chord of **three** notes is called a **triad**.

Play Mother's chord with your right hand only.

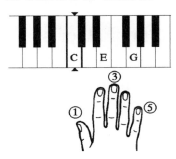

Here again are the notes in the **C Major** Family but this time with the mother chord.

Here is the father of the **C** Family.

He is a very important member of the family. What is the letter name of his note? ____

Father has a chord. It is built like this. Mother is number 1.

What number is Father? ____

Play Father's chord with your right hand only.

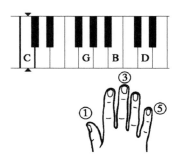

Here are the notes in the **C Major** Family.
Can you put in the mother and father chords?

Here is another member of the C Family.

She is the daughter.
What is the letter name
of her note? ____

The daughter has a
chord like this.
Mother and Father
are numbers 1 and 5.
What number is Daughter?   ____

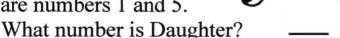

Play Daughter's
chord with your
right hand only.

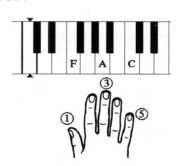

Here is the **Inner Family** in the key of **C**.

Mother is chord 1 because she is built on the first note. Name her notes. __ __ __

Father is chord 5 because he is built on the fifth note. Name his notes. __ __ __

Daughter is chord 4 because she is built on the fourth note. Name her notes. __ __ __

Write in the mother, father and daughter chords in the key of **C Major**.

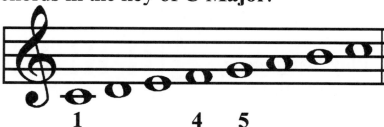

1   4   5

There is a mother, father and daughter chord in every musical family.

Here are the notes in the **G Major** Family.
Write in the mother, daughter and father chords.

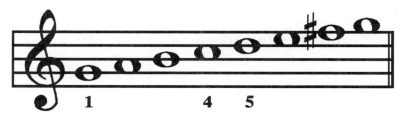

Use your right hand
to play
   Mother's
      chord →

Daughter's
   chord →

Father's
  chord →

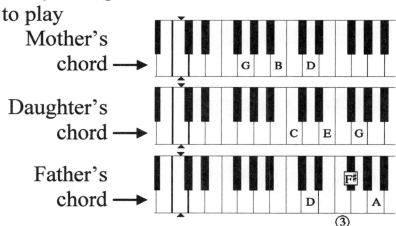

Have fun and write the three
chords for the **Inner Family**
in the key of **F major**.

Next-door Neighbours

Imagine that the **G** and **F** Families are the next-door neighbours of the **C** Family.

The **C** Family has
no sharps or flats.

The **G** Family has one sharp
(F sharp).

The **F** Family has one flat
(B flat).

This is the start of the **Magic Circle of Keys**.

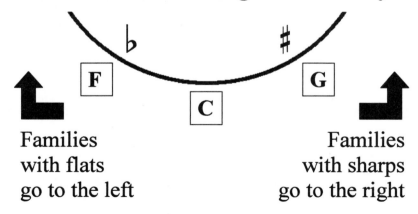

Families
with flats
go to the left

Families
with sharps
go to the right

You will meet other neighbours later.

Family Names

Let us look again at the family of **C**.

Just as you have more than one name, the **Inner Family** also have other names.

Mother is **chord 1**
and her other name is
the **Tonic**.

Father is **chord 5**
and his other name is
the **Dominant**.

Daughter is **chord 4**
and her other name is
the **Subdominant**.

Here are three chords for you to draw and then play. Listen to the sounds they make.

 Put in the correct key signature. Draw in the daughter chord - (4) - the **subdominant** chord in the family of **F Major**.

Put in the correct key signature. Draw in the mother chord - (1) - the **tonic** chord in the family of **G Major**.

 Draw in the father chord - (5) - the **dominant** chord in the family of **G Major** *without* the key signature.

Growing Chords

 You now know that the mother chord in the family of **C** looks like this. ➡

The note **C** is called the **root** because the chord grows from this note.

The note **E** is the **third** of the chord.

The note **G** is the **fifth** of the chord.

 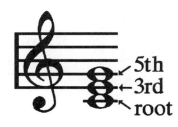

Here is the mother note in the family of **F**.

 Grow Mother's chord by drawing in the other two notes.

1

 Grow Father's chord in the family of **C**.

5

Now grow **two** chords for Daughter in the family of **G** from the **root** notes.

4

 Remember to play and listen carefully to all the chords.

Here are two more chords for you to grow.

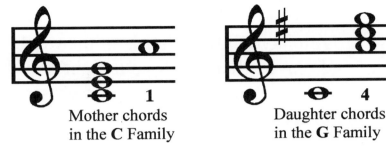

Mother chords
in the **C** Family

Daughter chords
in the **G** Family

As you can see, these chords have the same three notes. This often happens in families of keys. However, chord **CEG** in the **C** Family is always Mother and chord **CEG** in the **G** Family is always Daughter.

Mother C and **Daughter G** are *different* people.

Here is a little test!
Draw Father's chord (5) in the **C** Family and Mother's chord (1) in the **G** Family.

Using the Left Hand

So far you have drawn chords in the treble clef and played them with your right hand. Now you are also going to use the bass clef and your left hand.

Here is **chord 1** of **C major** for your right hand only.

Here is the same chord with the **root** note **in the bass clef** for your left hand.

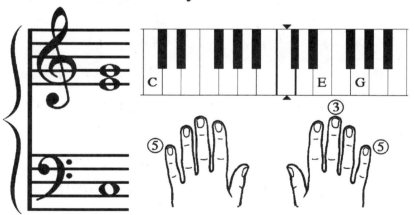

Play the top two notes with your right hand. Remember ⑤③⑤ are your finger numbers.

Here are Mother, Daughter and Father chords in the family of **C** shared between your two hands. Play and listen to these chords.

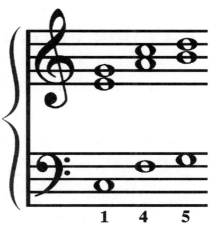

Here are the **root** notes for Mother, Daughter and Father chords in the family of **G Major**. Fill in the notes in the treble clef. Play and listen to the chords.

Fill in the notes in the treble clef for the Mother, Daughter and Father chords in the family of **F Major**. Play and listen to these chords.

A Quick Look Back

In every musical family, Mother is chord _,
Father is chord _ and Daughter is chord _.
In the family of **G Major**, Mother's note is
_, Father's note is _ and Daughter's note
is _. Mother's other name is the **t**____ and
Father's other name is the _____.
Daughter is the other member of the **Inner
Family**. Her other name is the
_____. The note
from which each chord grows
is called the **r**_____.

/10

Take Care!

Sometimes, a chord within one family has
the same notes as a chord within another.

Mother C and **Father F** are *different* people.

Harmony with the Inner Family

Here is a tune for you to play. It uses the three chords of the **Inner Family** of the key of **C Major**. Count two beats in each bar.

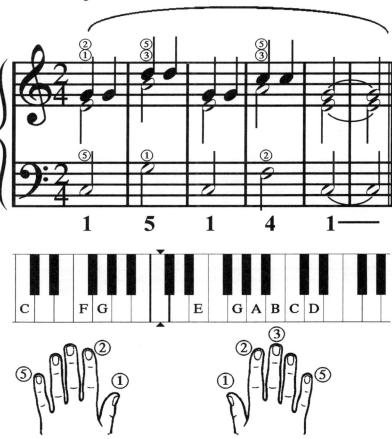

While you play, listen very carefully and notice how the chords fit the melody.

Here are the **Inner Family** chords of the key of **G Major**.

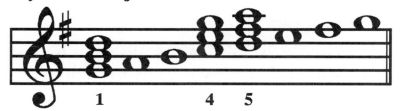

1 4 5

Draw Mother, Father and Daughter chords for this melody. First put the **root** note of each chord **in the bass** clef for your left hand.

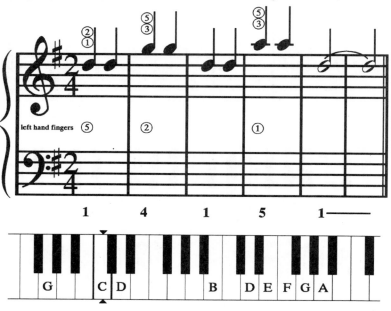

You can now play this piece with both hands. Count two beats in a bar.

Draw in the **Inner Family** chords for the key of **F Major**.

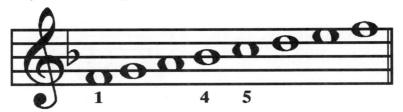

Now draw Mother, Father and Daughter chords for this melody. First put the **root** note of each chord **in the bass** clef.

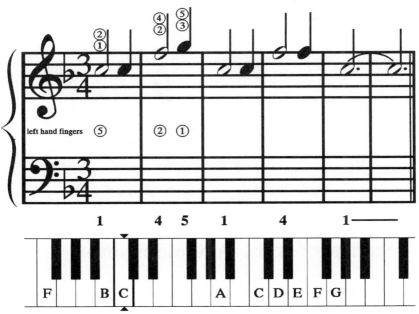

Play the piece with both hands. Count three beats in a bar. Listen carefully to the melody and the harmony.

Notes Can Change Places

You know a chord grows from its **root** and you know the names of the other

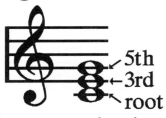
5th
←3rd
root

two notes in a triad - three-note chord.

Here are two ways to draw Mother **chord 1** of the **C Major** Family in **root position**. The first is **closed**. The second is **open**, so you may need to play **C** with the left hand.

Now draw Father **chord 5** in **C Major** in two different ways **in root position**. The **root** has been drawn **at the bottom** for you.

Draw Daughter **chord 4** in **C Major** in two different ways **in root position**. Put the **root** note **at the bottom** each time.

Play both chords and listen to their sounds.

Root Position

Here are the **root position chords** of the **Inner Family** of **C Major** drawn in two different ways. The **root** is **at the bottom**.

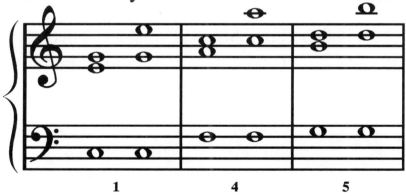

Play the chords with both hands and listen carefully to the different sounds they make.

First Inversion

The **root**, **3rd** and **5th** of a chord keep their names even when the notes change places.

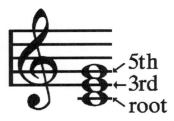

This is Mother **chord 1** in the **C Major** Family in **root position**.

We could draw the same chord with the

root at the top and the **3rd at the bottom**. This is still Mother chord 1 in **C Major** but we now call it

chord 1b because the **3rd** is **at the bottom**.

Draw Father **chord 5b** and Daughter **chord 4b** for the **C Major** Family. The **3rd** of each chord has been drawn at the bottom for you.

Play both chords and listen to their sounds.

A first inversion is a chord with the **3rd at the bottom**. Here are three first inversions (**1b**, **4b** and **5b**) shared between the hands.

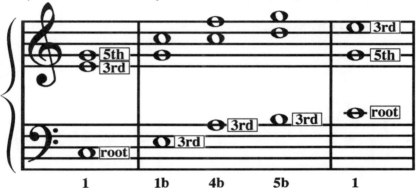

| 1 | 1b | 4b | 5b | 1 |

Play these chords. They make different sounds from the chords in root position.

1   1b

Draw Mother chord in the family of **G** in **root position** and in **first inversion**.

Now complete chords **1** and **1b** again shared between the two hands. Melody notes are given.

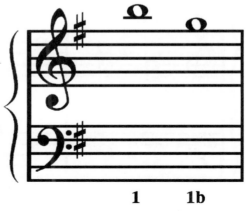

1   1b

Draw Mother chord in the family of **F** in **root** position and **first inversion**.

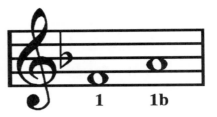

1   1b

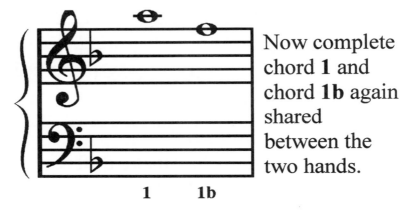

1   1b

Now complete chord **1** and chord **1b** again shared between the two hands.

Here are Mother, Father and Daughter chords for the family of **C Major**. They are in **root position** and **first inversion**. Play each chord and listen to the variety of sounds.

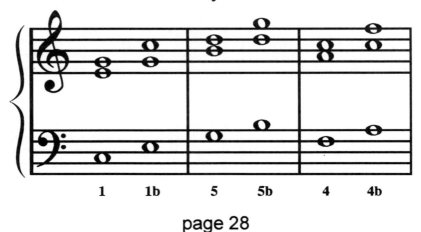

1   1b   5   5b   4   4b

Write Mother, Father and Daughter chords in **root position** and **first inversion** for the family of **G Major**.

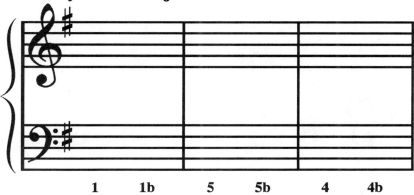

1	1b	5	5b	4	4b

Write the chords for the **Inner Family** of **F Major** in **root position** and **first inversion**.

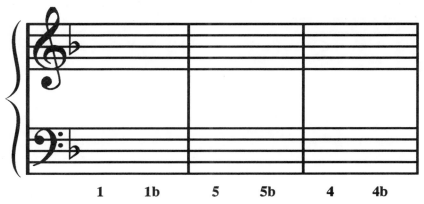

1	1b	5	5b	4	4b

It is important to practise these chords in the key of **C** and in the neighbouring keys of **G** and **F**. This helps you to move more easily between the families. Remember the magic circle of keys.

How Many Notes in a Chord?

A chord is two or more notes played together. Play and listen to these chords.

Here they are with the root in the bass clef.

Notice that we made the *two-note chord into a three-note chord* by **doubling the root**. Play these chords with both hands and listen to their sounds.

Play and Listen

Play these **G Major** tonic chords.

third doubled	third omitted
unpleasant sound	*hollow sound*

Now play these ***pleasant-sounding tonic chords.***
(a) all three notes with root doubled
(b) 5th omitted and root doubled
(c) all three notes with 5th doubled.

Double the root or fifth of a chord and *never* omit the third. Do *not* double the third - *yet*!

Harmonising a Melody

Here is a melody in the **C Major** Family.
Play the melody and listen to it.

Here is the same melody with harmony.
Play the harmonised melody and listen to
the difference in the sound.

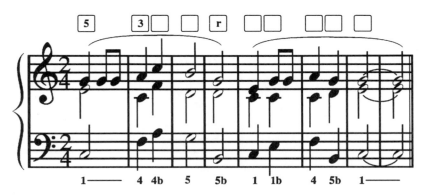

Put **r** or **3** or **5** in each empty box
to show whether the **root**, **3rd** or
5th note is at the top of the chord.
· How many were correct?

Over to you

Here are eight
C Major chords.

Use the chords to harmonise the melody
below using minims and crotchets. The
chord numbers are given to help you.

1   4   5b   1   1b   4   5   1

Broken Chords

Play this harmonised melody in the **G** Family.

Notice how the 3rd of a chord gives warmth to the harmony.

warm cold   **cold warm**

The same melody can be harmonised with the **chords broken up** in the left hand.

Pedalling – Try changing the pedal for each new chord. Understanding harmony helps you to pedal well.

Four-note Chords

You can harmonise two or more melody notes with the same chord. Look at these bars.

You can also harmonise the melody with three notes in the right hand and one note in the left.

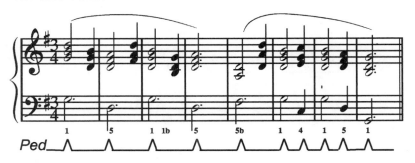

After you have played and pedalled this piece, circle in red all the **root** notes of each chord. You will be surprised how many have been **doubled**!

Look Ahead

Where do members go in musical families?

Mother goes
to Father.

  Father goes
to Mother.

Mother goes
to Daughter.

  Daughter goes
to Father.

Daughter goes
to Mother.

 Father chords prefer not
to go to Daughter chords!

Fill in the chords for this melody. Use one note for the left hand and two or three notes for the right hand.

Notice in bar 2 that Mother chord is used instead of Father chord for the note **D** because Daughter chord follows in bar 3. **Look ahead when filling in chords.**

Over to You

Here is a melody in the family of **G** for you to harmonise. The notes for the left hand have been put in. Add one or two notes to the melody for the right hand.

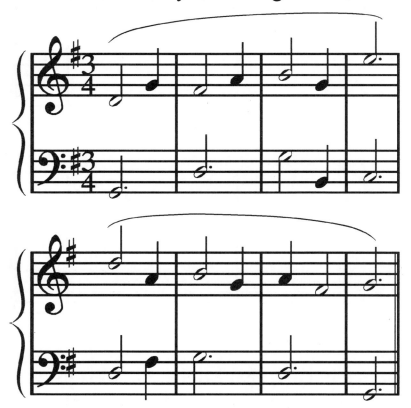

Do not double or omit the 3rd!

Here is the same melody in the **G** Family for you to harmonise. Notice that Mother is often the first chord. This time put some broken chords for the left hand to play.

Practise playing and singing your melody before harmonising it.

Music is Flexible

Let's not forget the **F** Family. They live
next to the **C** Family on the **Magic Circle**.

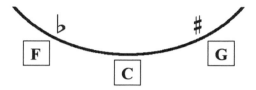

Here is a melody in **F Major** harmonised
in two ways, firstly with **block chords** and
then with **broken chords**.

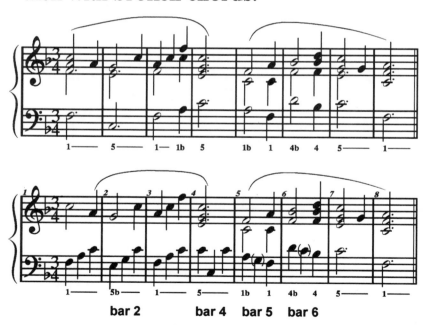

Refer to the music at the bottom of page 40 and use these words to fill the gaps below.

bar 2: The **5b** means _____ chord in ___ _____ with the ___ note at the bottom.

bar 4: The notes in the left hand make the music move by floating between the _____.

bar 5: Note **G** in the bracket is called a **passing note**. It links note **A** to note **F**.

bar 6: Note __ is a _____ _____ because it links note __ to note __.

Music is flexible, so remember to mix root position and 1st inversion chords when you harmonise the following melody.

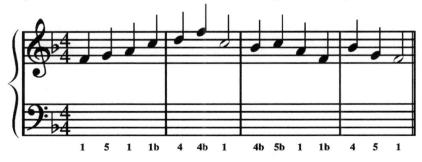

An Extra Note

You now know the **Inner Family**.

Chord 1	**Tonic**	Mother
Chord 5	**Dominant**	Father
Chord 4	**Subdominant**	Daughter

Father is a very important
family member. Here is
his chord in **C Major**.

Father chord can sometimes have four notes.
This extra note is seven up from the root.

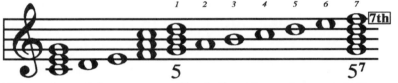

The chord is now called the **dominant 7th**.

Play these Father chords [5 5b 5^7 5^7b] with
your right hand and listen to their sounds.

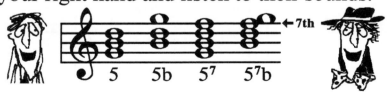

Hear the **softening effect** of the **extra note**.

Now play the chords shared between the hands and listen for the **softening effect** in the **dominant 7th** chord.

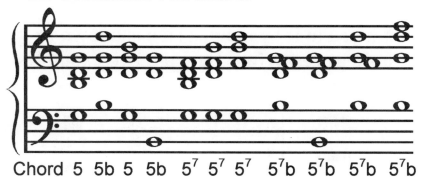

Chord 5 5b 5 5b 5^7 5^7 5^7 5^7b 5^7b 5^7b 5^7b

Just as the root, **3rd** and **5th** notes keep their identity no matter where they appear, so does the **7th** note of a chord.

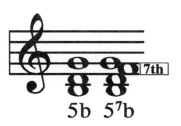

5b 5^7b

5b 5^7b

Complete these **dominant** chords in the families of **F** and **G Major**.

The **5th** notes have been put in to help you.

Remember that **5^7b** will have the **3rd** at the bottom.

5b 5^7b

Resolving

The **7th** note of the dominant Father chord likes to fall onto the note below, as if attracted to it by magic. This is known in music as **resolving**. Here are two examples in the family of **C Major**.

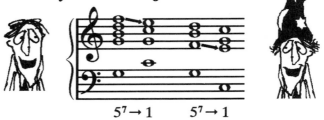

$5^7 \rightarrow 1$ $5^7 \rightarrow 1$

Play and enjoy these dominant 7th chords in the musical neighbours of the **C Family**.

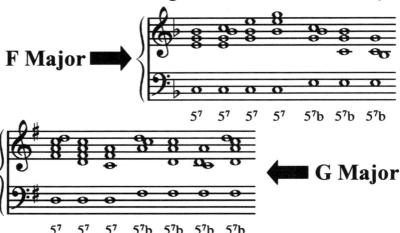

F Major ➡

5^7 5^7 5^7 5^7 5^7b 5^7b 5^7b

⬅ **G Major**

5^7 5^7 5^7 5^7b 5^7b 5^7b 5^7b

Never double the 7th in a dominant chord.

Now there are four

Each **Inner Family** now has **four** chords.

Chord 1	**Tonic**
Chord 4	**Subdominant**
Chord 5	**Dominant**
Chord 5^7	**Dominant 7th**

Here are all four chords for you to play in each of the **C**, **F** and **G Major** Families.

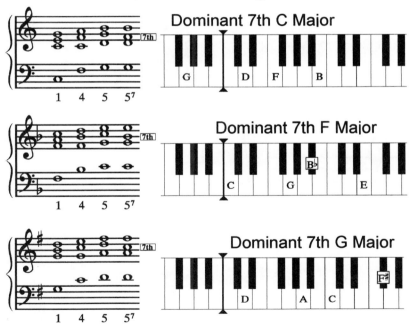

Dominant 7th C Major

Dominant 7th F Major

Dominant 7th G Major

All twelve chords are in root position.

Now there are eight

Each of the **Inner Family** chords can be drawn in **root position** or **first inversion**. Here are the **eight** chords for **C Major**.

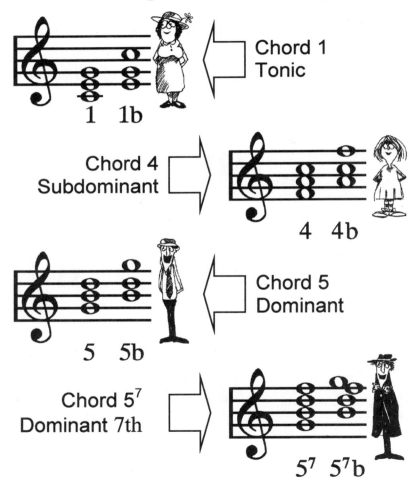

Chord 1
Tonic

1   1b

Chord 4
Subdominant

4   4b

Chord 5
Dominant

5   5b

Chord 5^7
Dominant 7th

5^7 5^7b

Here is a mixture of chords for our three musical families. Play them and fill in the empty boxes underneath the chords.

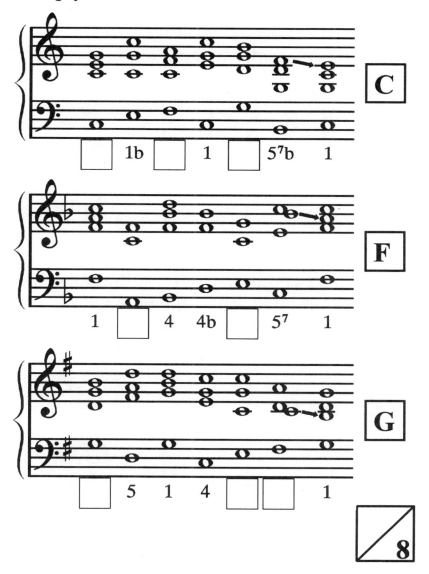

It's decision time

How do we choose between the father chord and the dominant 7th chord? The answer is in the sounds they make.
Play this example without the extra note.

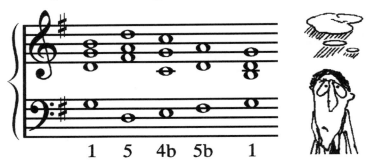

1   5   4b   5b   1

Now play and listen to the softening effect of the dominant 7th as the note **C** falls like magic onto the note **B** below, giving us that satisfying **resolving** sound.

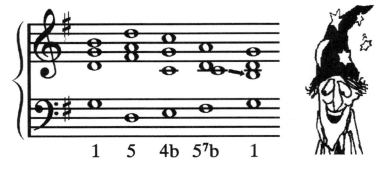

1   5   4b   5⁷b   1

A Perfect Cadence

When you reach the end of a piece of music you need a very 'final feeling'. For this reason, pieces often end with Father or Dominant 7th chord going to Mother chord. This is called a **perfect cadence**.

chord 5 to chord 1   **chord 5⁷ to chord 1**

Complete these perfect cadences with Father going home to Mother. Use dominant 7th chords resolving onto tonic chords.

Trust Your Ears

In the **C** Major Family, the note **F** has been harmonised by Daughter chord. Until now, she has been the only member of the **Inner Family** with that note. With the arrival of Father's extra note, we have a choice.

chord 4   **chord 5⁷**

Here are examples of how these chords can be used. In the first example the dominant 7th does **not** appear and the sound is dull.

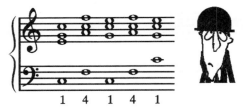

1   4   1   4   1

In these next two the sound is much richer.

1   5⁷   1   4   1   1   4   1   5⁷   1

Complete the five chords in each of these examples and fill in the empty boxes.
Trust your ears to make 'sound' decisions.

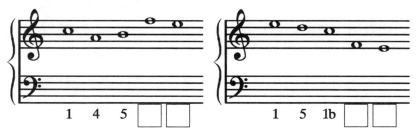

An Imperfect Cadence

We use this cadence to create an impression of rest at a point where the piece does not end but where a 'breath' is needed. You can think of an **imperfect** cadence like a **comma** and a **perfect** cadence like a **full stop**.

chord 1 to chord 5   **chord 4 to chord 5**

For an **imperfect cadence**, either chord can be used to go to Father chord.

The Plagal Cadence

Daughter chord going to Mother chord is called a **plagal** cadence.

chord 4   to   chord 1

This combination of chords does not give as effective an ending as the perfect cadence.

Play and compare these two examples.

plagal 4 1   **perfect** 5 1

Summary

Cadence	First Chord ➡	Second chord
Perfect	Father *dominant*	Mother *tonic*
Imperfect	Mother / Daughter *tonic / subdominant*	Father *dominant*
Plagal	Daughter *subdominant*	Mother *tonic*

A Final Look Back

Use each word once only to fill in the gaps.

Mother tonic Father dominant
Daughter subdominant perfect
imperfect plagal root position
first inversion root 3rd 5th 7th 15

A chord with the root at the bottom is in
_____. When the third of
the chord is at the bottom, the chord is a
_____. You can double the
_____ or _____ of a chord. You should
not double or omit the _____ of a chord.
A dominant 7th is a Father chord with an
extra note which is the ____ note up from
the root. Daughter chords like to go to
_____ or _____ chords. Father
chords prefer not to go to _____ chords.
A dominant chord going to the _____
chord is called a _____ cadence. The
_____ chord going to the tonic
chord is called a _____ cadence. Chord
1 or 4 going to the _____ chord
is called an _____ cadence.

Father or Daughter?

Use the dominant 7th or the subdominant to complete the chords in the following melodies. Put the number of the chord you use in the empty box underneath the chord.

Helpful hints

(1) use the magic of Father's dominant 7th resolving onto Mother's tonic chord.
(2) remember Daughter's subdominant chord wants to go to Father or Mother.
(3) use 1st inversions even of Father's dominant 7th chord.
(4) play and sing the melody to find **clues** before you harmonise it.

First melody (four bars)

Second melody (four bars)

Third melody (eight bars)

You are now ready to harmonise three well-known tunes using lots of chords.

Do you recognise this tune? Harmonise it by drawing in broken chords in the left hand. Two bars have been filled in for you

This tune is about the 10th century saint of Bohemia whose feast day is Sept. 28th. Draw 2/3 notes in treble & 1 note in bass.

This is a Scottish tune which is sung at midnight on New Year's Eve.

For he's a jolly good fellow

Good King Wenceslas

Auld Lang Syne

List of terms

broken chord   the notes of a chord played one after the other

cadence   the half or full close of a musical phrase or section

    imperfect   any chord going to chord 5 suggesting a pause for breath

    perfect   chord 5 going to chord 1 with a strong feeling of ending

    plagal   chord 4 going to chord 1 with a weak feeling of ending

chord   two or more notes that are played together

    in close position   the notes of a chord are as close together as possible

    in open position   the notes of a chord are spread widely

chord 1   tonic chord in root position

    1b   tonic chord in first inversion

    4   subdominant chord in root position

    4b   subdominant chord in first inversion

    5   dominant chord in root position

    5b   dominant chord in first inversion

    5^7   dominant 7th chord in root position

chord 5^7b   dominant 7th chord in first inversion

dominant [Father]	5th note of a scale and the chord grown from that note: e.g. G and G-B-D in the scale of C Major
dominant 7th	dominant chord with its 3rd, 5th & 7th notes: e.g. G-B-D-F in the C Major scale
doubling	the same note (root or 5th but not usually the 3rd) is used twice in the same chord
first inversion	chord with its 3rd note at the bottom
resolving	movement of a note or chord to a more satisfying note or chord: e.g. chord 5^7 to chord 1
root	note from which a chord grows: e.g. C is the root of the tonic chord of C Major
root position	the root of a chord is at the bottom or in the bass
subdominant [Daughter]	4th note of a scale and the chord grown from that note: e.g. F and F-A-C in the C Major scale
triad	a three-note chord: e.g. the tonic triad C-E-G of the C Major scale
tonic [Mother]	1st note of a scale and the chord grown from that note: e.g. C and C-E-G in the C Major scale

Treble clef, bass clef, notes and letter names. Time names and values; dotted notes, tied notes and rests.
Accidentals. Tones and semitones.
Key signatures and scales (C, G, D & F Major).
Degrees of the scale, intervals and tonic triads.
Simple time signatures and bar-lines.
Writing music and answering rhythms.
Musical terms dictionary and list of signs.

ISBN 0-9516940-8-1

Major key signatures and scales to 3 sharps or 3 flats.
A, D and E minor key signatures and scales.
Degrees of the scale and intervals. Tonic triads and accidentals.
Piano keyboard, tones and semitones.
Simple time signatures. Grouping notes and rests. Triplets.
Two ledger lines below and above the staves.
Writing four-bar rhythms
More musical terms and signs.

ISBN 1-898771-02-2

Major and minor key signatures to 4 sharps or 4 flats.
Harmonic and melodic minor scales.
Degrees of the scale, intervals and tonic triads.
Simple and compound time signatures. Grouping notes and rests. Transposition at the octave.
More than two ledger lines.
Writing four-bar rhythms. Anacrusis. Phrases.
More musical terms and signs.

ISBN 1-898771-00-6

All key signatures to 5 sharps or 5 flats. Alto clef; chromatic scale, double sharps and flats. Technical names of notes in the diatonic scale. Simple and compound time: duple, triple, quadruple. Primary triads: tonic, subdominant and dominant.
All diatonic intervals up to an octave. Recognising ornaments.
Four-bar rhythms and rhythms to words.
Families of orchestral instruments and their clefs.
More musical terms, including French.

ISBN 1-898771-01-4

All key signatures to 7 sharps or 7 flats. Tenor clef and scales.
Compound intervals: major, minor, perfect, diminished and augmented. Irregular time signatures: quintuple and septuple.
Tonic, supertonic, subdominant and dominant chords.
Writing at concert pitch. Short and open score. Orchestral instruments in detail. Composing a melody for instrument or voice. Perfect, imperfect and plagal cadences.
More musical terms, including German.

ISBN 0-9516940-9-X